This Book Belongs to
Sean B,
Joe B-
Jesufe B.
if lost Call:
180-786-9708
give Back if found Now
Thank you.

CRAYON

written by
H. I. Peeples

illustrated by
Steve Haefele

A CALICO BOOK
Published by Contemporary Books, Inc.

A Calico Book
Published by Contemporary Books, Inc.
180 North Michigan Avenue, Chicago, Illinois 60601
Copyright © 1988 by The Kipling Press
Text Copyright © 1988 by Robert Cwiklik & Russell Shorto
Illustrations Copyright © 1988 by Steve Haefele
All Rights Reserved.

Art Direction by Tilman Reitzle
Library of Congress Catalog Card Number: 88-19325
International Standard Book Number: 0-8092-4467-5
Manufactured in the United States of America

Published simultaneously in Canada by Beaverbooks, Ltd.
195 Allstate Parkway, Valleywood Business Park
Markham, Ontario L3R 4T8 Canada

S ometimes,
when the weather is
bad, life can seem
very gloomy and
colorless. Look out
the window—a world
of gray skies and
rain. But there is
something that you
can do... something
that every kid loves.
And you don't have to
go outside to do it!

3

That's right! One sure way to put some color into your life on a rainy day (or any day) is with a box of brightly colored crayons. Look at those beautiful colors. Smell that familiar smell!

Imagine being able to actually borrow colors from a rainbow in the sky. That's what owning a box of crayons lets you do. With crayons, you can create all kinds of colorful pictures by putting the rainbow to work in your own living room. But have you ever wondered where crayons come from?

Crayons are made at large factories all over the country. First, color is made from various chemicals that are mixed together with water in large mixing tanks. When this mixing is completed, the color, or *pigment*, is filtered to remove excess water and then scraped off the filter trays.

The pigment is baked in a kiln so that it dries completely, and then it passes through a machine that grinds the pigment into a fine powder. Now the most important ingredient for your crayons—the color— is ready to be used!

Crayons are made of color, *paraffin*, and something called *stearic acid*. The paraffin is a by-product of oil production and comes from an oil refinery. It is stored at the crayon factory in huge storage tanks outside. These tanks are kept warm because, like wax, the paraffin will harden if it is allowed to cool.

The foreman of the crayon factory chooses the color of the day. Every day means a different color—for example, on the red day, only red crayons are made. When the factory is ready to begin making crayons, the warm, gloopy paraffin is sent through pipes and into the factory.

9

After a batch of hot liquid paraffin is dumped into a huge vat inside the factory, the color is added. The color, a fine powder, is poured from a sack into the vat and stirred well. At this stage, stearic acid is added to the mixture. This is what gives crayons their distinctive smell.

When the color is thoroughly blended with the hot paraffin, the mixture is poured onto a flat tray with thousands of holes that lead into crayon-shaped slots. The slots quickly fill up with the mixture. Cold water circulates around the slots and the mixture cools down very quickly.

11

When the mixture becomes cold, it hardens. A red light flashes on. Now we have crayons! When the machine operator pushes a button, the machine turns the tray upside-down and all the crayons are pushed out of their holes.

The crayons sprout like a field of colored stalks onto a large tray. Here a very important person with good eyes checks the crayons to make sure they are made properly. If any have bubbles in them, or if any are broken or mis-shaped, they are put back into the vat of hot paraffin and melted down again.

The crayons are then collected in neat stacks of colored sticks. They are ready to be "dressed." The crayons are put on a conveyor belt and brought to the labeling machine. This machine coats each crayon with glue and then wraps two labels around it. Using two labels makes the crayon stronger.

Each label will tell you where the crayons were made and what colors they are. Did you know that the largest crayon manufacturing company in the United States makes two million crayons every year?

15

Once the crayons are wrapped, they are crated up and brought to a storage area. There they are placed next to other crates containing the same color. It's important that the factory has a large supply of all different colors.

When the storage area is running low on a certain color, the foreman tells the factory to make some more. "We need more 'sunlight yellow,'" he might call out. Keeping a careful eye on the crayon supply is important because crayon boxes are made of a selection of colors. Without one of these colors, the factory would be unable to deliver any crayons.

Finally, the crayons leave the storage area and are sent to the packing machine. This machine fills several compartments with one color each. Then the crayons are funneled into a box so that there is the right assortment of different colors.

The machine sorts the colors into packages of eight, sixteen, or up to sixty-four different colors. This depends on how many different colors a factory can make. Some colors are very special and difficult to make. The recipes for these colors are kept secret. The boxes of crayons are then crated up and taken to the stores.

At last, from the stores, they reach the homes of children who can now use them to add color to their lives. They can choose from colors such as lemon yellow, cornflower, periwinkle, brick red, spring green, magenta, and many, many more.

There's nothing like a brand-new box of crayons. Look how sharp those lovely new points are! Smell that fresh smell! See how beautiful those colors are—just like a rainbow!

21

So the next time you look up at a rainbow in the sky, remember that no matter what your favorite color is, you can probably find it—or something pretty close to it — in your own box of crayons.